My Dear Grandchildren,

I started this book for you children, the moment you were born Marion, but it took rather longer than I expected. Then Ewenie arrived, so I started another book for your cousins, so I have been working on the two books for some time. Anyway I am quite determined that both families will have their books by this Christmas 1980. As you see its the 28th November now, (my 65th birthday incidentally) I am running it a bit close!

As I have worked on these books, they have become more and more involved and taken longer. The original idea was just to have a picture of a flower on one page, and the name of the flower on the opposite page. That looked a little bleak however.

So I started to write a little bit about each flower, and then decorating the written side, until I have ended up sometimes, having almost as much painting on the written side, as on the other.

Then it was thought a good idea, if I could put a verse about each flower opposite it. Easier said than done.

Lots of poets write about the popular flowers such as Roses, Daisies, and Honeysuckles etc; but you try and find a poem about a Knapweed, Fumitory, Scabious or an Umbelliferae!

Then the wonderful poems by professional poets showed up my efforts so badly that I thought it would be better to have them all written in my own funny doggerel verse.

So my doggeral verses you have, and in them I have tried to let the flowers talk to you as opposed to those who think they have to talk to the flowers.

I must also say here if it had not been for Grandpa, the verses would have been much worse than they are. All the way through the book he has endeavoured to correct my erratic English and spelling, and with the rhymes he has helped a tremendous amount. When I was stuck for a word he produced one for me, he rewrote many of the lines in the poems, and some poems he wrote entirely. (See "O")

He also helped with the rhythm and stopped me many a time from behaving like that old man of Japan, who's rhymes they never will scan, because "he liked to get as many words into the last line as he possibly can".

Also I do hope that G K Chesterton is not turning in his grave at the way I have borrowed his words for my poem on Travellers Joy.

The whole idea of this book is to arouse your interest in the flowers and nature around you. The more you learn, the more fascinating it becomes, and I have certainly discovered much that is interesting and new to me while writing these two books for you and your cousins.

So I hope this inspires you to go out and look for flowers, and bring them back and to identify them. Then why not press them between newspapers, and stick them in a book, and write under each flower, its name, and the date and place where you found it, and see how many you can get.

I think I have written this book for Mummie, almost as much as for you children, so I hope you all enjoy it, and that it makes you laugh a bit and I hope learn a bit too.

Grandma.

A FLORAL ABC

by

Elizabeth Cameron

for my daughter Kirstie

and her children

Marion Elizabeth Victoria Evans

Rachel Fiona Clare Evans

Veronica Lucy Margaret Evans

John Wiley & Sons Canada Limited
Toronto □ New York □ Chichester □ Brisbane

A is for Anemone

Anemone nemorosa

The family is called Ranunculaceae, (RAN-UN-Q-LAY-SEE) and a cousin of that very well known flower the buttercup.

It is also well known as the wind flower, as the word anemone comes from the Greek word for wind "anemos".

Pliny, the early Italian writer and historian, said "The floure openeth itself, but when the wynde bloweth." And if you think Grandma's spelling is worse than usual, its an old English translation and is meant to be like that - So there.

It is also known as the Candlemas Cap in Dorset, as it is at Candlemas, 2nd February, that it first appears there, but up here in Ross-shire it is much later.

In mythology Anemone was a lovely nymph, beloved by Zephyr, the God of the West. This aroused the jealousy of The Goddess Flora, who fancied Zephyr herself. So to clear her path, she transformed Anemone into the little Wind Flower we know today. Zephyr took no further interest in her, and abandoned her to Boreas, the North Wind, who woos her in early spring. That is why Anemone is said to represent all those forsaken and forlorn, and is rather a sad little flower.

I thrive in the woods and under the trees
And really enjoy a nice fresh breeze.
Come early spring, I produce pale flowers
Inspite of the cold and April showers,
While many a mortal just shiver and sneeze.

Collected from the roadside Allangrange Farm April 78.

B is for Bluebell

Endymion non-scriptus

I have called this flower a Bluebell, because at the moment you live in England and thats what they call it there. Because I am your Scottish Grandma, you must learn from me that it really is the Wild Hyacinth, and the Bluebell is quite a different flower. Before the 16th century this flower was called Hyacinthus Angelica, such a much nicer name than Endymion non-scriptus which the botanists gave it. It does not even belong to the same family, and is not even a relation of the Bluebell, but belongs to the Liliaceae family (LIE-LI-A-SAY), and is a cousin of the Martagon Lily.

The legend of this flower is that Hyacinth was a handsome youth, much loved by the God Apollo. One day they were playing quoits, which was a game they used to play in Greece, and Apollo accidently hit his young friend on the head and killed him. Apollo was very upset and sad as he was unable to save the life of Hyacinth, but so that we should always remember him, he was able to change him into this beautiful flower, which makes a lovely carpet of blue, every spring in our shady woods.

The Hyacinth grows from a bulb, and from this bulb in the old days, they used to make glue. If you dig up and scrape the bulb, you will find it is covered with a slime which makes a very strong glue. However dont do this, as it kills the flower, and we want to preserve our wild flowers. It does no harm to pick the flowers, but try not to trample on the leaves as when they are damaged they are unable to get the food they need to live, and so they die. So watch where you step!

Quoits was a game, Apollo did play,
Till one day Hyacinth got in the way.
The quoit hit Hyacinth bang on the head.
He fell to the ground and lay there dead.
Apollo did weep and was full of remorse
But alas could do nothing to save him of course.
So he then cast a spell (the Gods had the power)
And the poor boy was changed to this beautiful flower.

The real Bluebell

Picked on my first visit to Wayton 29" May 78.

is for Cowslip

Primula veris

This flower belongs to the Primulace family, which is pronounced PRIM-U-LACE-AY. It is a large family and there are many cousins, one which you know very well the Primrose.
Alas the Cowslip has been very over picked because it used to be gathered to make Cowslip wine, so now you dont see so many, so you should leave them alone if you find them growing wild, and not pick them. They grow in medows and on banks, mostly in England. There are alas very few in Scotland, so I picked this one in the Spring from my own garden where I have just a few growing.
Do you know why they are called Cowslips?
Because they used to be called cuslyppe or cuslop which was the old English word for cowdung or cowpat. It then became cowslop and a little later the name was changed again to the more delicate name of Cowslip because it was said to grow where ever the cow left a cowpat.

I grew where the cow slopped in olden days,
But now I am rare because of mans ways,
Who pick me for wine,
To please those who dine,
And who drink themselves into a haze.

Cow - slip - slopping

Picked Allangrange Garden May 78   EC.

D is for Daisy

Bellis perennis

This is a very small flower of the very large family of Compositae. (COM-POS-IT-AY) I am sure you know one of its cousins the Dandelion.

The word Daisy comes from "Days eye" which it was called originally, as it opens in the morning when the sun gets up and closes in the evening when the sun disappears. Many poems and songs have been written about the Daisy and our Robert Burns wrote of it as "weemodest crimson tippet flower"

Have you ever made a Daisy chain to wear round your neck, or like a crown in your hair? There's a little rhyme which says

> The girls who wear a Daisy chain
> Grow up pretty, never plain.

So you'd better start making one quickly. As you see I have put Daisy chains around this page.

The Daisy grows almost everywhere, practically all the year round and it loves short grass especially, like our lawns. Its leaves grow very flat to the ground, so animals are unable to eat them, and the garden mower passes over them, — so it survives.

> I love to grow on the lawn where you tread
> But weekly the mower will chop off my head,
> I find life exhausting, and rather a strain,
> As I have to start growing all over again.

EC.

Picked outside the studio window September 78

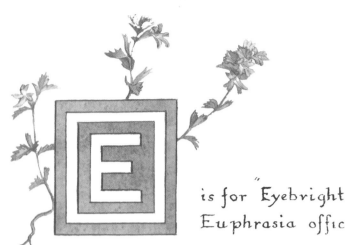

E is for "Eyebright
Euphrasia officinalis

This little flower with its difficult Latin
name, has an even worse family name which
is Scrophulariacae
It is a tiny tiny little flower which grows more or
less everywhere from June to Sept. The flowers are
collected for medical purposes, and made into such things
as eye lotions, hence the name "Eyebright."
It has a very important and large cousin, which I expect
you know, the Foxglove. Is it not strange that such
a little plant and such a large one all belong to the
same family. I picked this flower at Allangrange,
in July, up the back road.

LOTION
Specially made
for
Rachel Evans

I am a little eyebright, humble and small,
Some people never see me at all.
I flower in June, the Summer through.
My flowers are white, and touched with blue.
I thrive on the moor, in hedgerow or lane,
I like lots of sun and not too much rain.
But dont ignore me when passing by
My flowers make a lotion to sooth your eye.

Picked by Munlochy War Memorial 77

F is for Fumitory

Fumaria officinalis.

This pretty little weed is a member of the Papeveraceae (PAPA-VER-A-SAY) and is a cousin of the poppy, which looks so very different.

Its name comes from France where it is called Fume terre, which means smoke of the earth. The reason given for this is that they say the grey green rather fluffy leaves look rather like smoke. I think someone must have had a very keen imagination to think of that explanation. Much more likely I think is that if you pull the plant up by the root, it does smell a little like smoke and whats more the juice makes your eyes smart and weep, the same way as smoke does. It grows almost everywhere and is quite a problem as a weed, especially on light soils, and everyone who farms and gardens, knows this plant and does not always appreciate it!!

However it has long been used as a medical herb, and is still used by herbalists today for complaints of the liver and for jaundice, that disease which makes you turn all yellow.

The Gypsies consider this plant very important, and use it a lot for medical causes and it is a great favorite of theirs.

It has a funny little flower, and very unusual as can be told by its local names which includes Babes in the Cradle, Gods fingers and Thumbs, Ladies Shoes, and Wax Dolls, and whats more most of these names are the inventions of the people of Somerset, so they have a good imagination!

Fumitory means the smoke of the earth,
But here where I grow by the Inverness Firth
In the Allangrange garden, I do not smoke.
I'm a tangled weed, which is just not a joke
For Mr Donaldson, who dislikes me intensly
Which is sad, as I like here immensely.
So I think I'll just stay, in order to tease,
As I do so enjoy embracing his peas.

Picked in Allangrange Kitchen Garden. July 1978

G

is for Great Bindweed

Calystegia sepium

A member of the CON - VOL - VUL - ACE - AE family, which is a very long word, which is why I have written it spaced out as pronouned.   It is the largest convolvulus which grows in this country, and in some parts it is called Bellbine. You will see another smaller convolvulace in this book which has crept in under the letter "S".

There are lovely convolvulus's which grow in warmer countries, of beautiful blues, But I love our beautiful white one.

I picked this one off the fence in front of Old Allangrange House in the month of September.

I am truthfully a convolvulus of noble birth,
Though my grand garden cousins treat me with mirth,
They refer to me scornfully as just a "weed"!
But I'll grow and thrive, where they cant succeed.
I climb over everything, I twist and I wind,
Over all in my way, till the hedgrow is lined
With my beautiful flowers of white.

From outside Old Allangrange House 1977

is for Honeysuckle

Lonicera periclymenum

The Honeysuckle belongs to the Caprifoliaceae family, (CAP-RI-FOLIA-AY-SAY.) which we have not met before.

It is an endearing, sweet scented, twining and climbing plant, which scrambles through our hedges and woods.

Shakespeare speaks of it as gentle and entwining, but it can actually be quite a killer, as it twines itself clockwise around young saplings, and squeezes them into a spiral.

It flowers usually twice a year, in June and September, and visit it in the evening, just at dusk, as at this moment its scent is very strong and very sweet.

It has two common names, Honeysuckle and Woodbine. Honeysuckle, because at the base of each floret nectar is held, and if you pluck it and suck it, you can taste the honey, as every child knows.   Woodbine because of the way it it twines itself around it neighbours, which can end in disaster, if the neighbour happens to be young, as it is literally a woodbinder.

Woodbine, such a pretty old fashioned English name, has been entirely spoilt for me and my generation, as at the time of the first World War they produced a cheap cigarette which they called "Woodbine".   Infact Woodbine almost came to be another word meaning a cheap cigarette.   As for local names, Somerset as usual produces the most origonal "Gramophone horns".

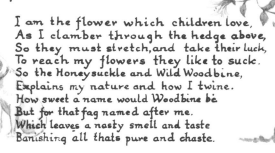

I am the flower which children love,
As I clamber through the hedge above,
So they must stretch, and take their luck,
To reach my flowers they like to suck.
So the Honeysuckle and Wild Woodbine,
Explains my nature and how I twine.
How sweet a name would Woodbine be
But for that fag named after me.
Which leaves a nasty smell and taste
Banishing all thats pure and chaste.

Collected from the wood behind Allangrange. September 1978

The hol-ly & the iv-y when they are both full grown of
all the trees that are in the wood The hol-ly bears the crown.

is for Ivy

Hedera helix

The Ivy belongs to the Araliacae family (A-RAIL-I-A-SAY) and is all on its own and has no cousins.

It is about the only plant that flowers in the late Autumn, and it is usually covered with insects, as it is the only source of honey they have at that time of the year. It produces its berries by Christmas.

It uses the trunks of other trees, and buildings to climb up, as it was not given a strong enough one to support itself. However it is not greedy and takes nothing from the bush or tree it is clambering over, and produces all its own food from its own roots.

The Holly and Ivy have been associated with each other for a very long time, and though today we think of them mainly as Christmas decorations, they were believed to have magical powers to drive demons away, long before the Christians adopted them. The Druids, who were the ancient British priests, before we became Christians, used their magical powers to drive away demons and goblins from the cows and to stop them from turning the milk and butter sour. This seemed to be a favorite pastime of goblins in these old days, so a bunch of Ivy and Holly was hung in the cow byre for protection.

So the Ivy and the Holly were brought into our homes to protect us from evil spirits, which was the origonal reason why we decorate our homes at Christmas time. However though we still sing of the "Holly and the Ivy" in our carols, we seem to have forgotten about the Ivy in our homes. Why? Just because it has no red berries! It is so much more graceful than the holly in the house and if you happen to live in a town, cheaper to obtain than Holly!

Before Christ was born, that first Christmas day
I aided the Druids keep the goblins at bay.
Along with the Holly, I hung in the byre,
Warding off spirits who turned the milk sour.
We came to your home for the very same reason
To keep evil out from this festival season.
For centuries at Christmas together we've been.
But now its the Holly that only is seen.
I am no longer wanted - nor is my magic,
So spare me a tear — my story is tragic.

Hidden in the picture opposite are 2 pigs, 2 ducks, 1 bird, 2 boys heads.

From the walls of the ruined Chapel — Allangrange November 77.

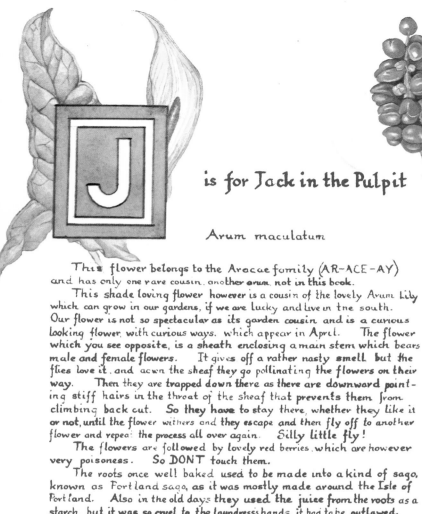

J

is for Jack in the Pulpit

Arum maculatum

This flower belongs to the Aracae family (AR-ACE-AY) and has only one rare cousin, another arum, not in this book.

This shade loving flower however is a cousin of the lovely Arum Lily which can grow in our gardens, if we are lucky and live in the south. Our flower is not so spectacular as its garden cousin and is a curious looking flower, with curious ways, which appear in April. The flower which you see opposite, is a sheath enclosing a main stem which bears male and female flowers. It gives off a rather nasty smell but the flies love it, and down the sheaf they go pollinating the flowers on their way. Then they are trapped down there as there are downward pointing stiff hairs in the throat of the sheaf that prevents them from climbing back out. So they have to stay there, whether they like it or not, until the flower withers and they escape and then fly off to another flower and repeat the process all over again. Silly little fly!

The flowers are followed by lovely red berries, which are however very poisoness. So DONT touch them.

The roots once well baked used to be made into a kind of sago, known as Portland sago, as it was mostly made around the Isle of Portland. Also in the old days they used the juice from the roots as a starch, but it was so cruel to the laundress's hands, it had to be outlawed.

Because of the rather curios formation of this flower it earned some rude names, like the Orchid, which we shall read about later, in fact it got quite a reputation as a naughty little sexy flower!

Jack in the Pulpit, was trying to keep
His congregation from going to sleep.
On and on he raved about hell,
Their evil ways he hoped to dispel.
They sat through it all with minds astray,
Thinking of life and work and play.
I'm said to aid their evil deeds,
By sowing lustful thoughts and seeds,
But man is weak and very silly
As what am I, but a harmless lily

The last flower of season Flatford Mills June 79

is for Knapweed

Centaurea nigra.

This belongs to the Compositae family, (COM-POS-IT-AY) so is a cousin of the Daisy, who we have already met.

It is a very tough and wiry little flower which grows all over the country, rare in the Highlands, though I did pick this one by the roadside going north from Evanton. In the old days it was used as a medicine to treat sores, bruises and even sore throats.

It has a very hard little knob for its head, as its second name "Hardhead" suggests. The stems are also very tough and it is very difficult to pick or cut, which makes it quite a problem weed for the farmer on grazing land, as not even the cows will eat it, as they find it too tough and not to their taste.

Beside the name Hardhead, it has a lot of local nicknames, such as Shaving brush, Topknots, Drummer Heads, Chimney sweep, and Bottle brush which are all names which explain themselves.

This flower was used of old by maidens to tell their future in love. They would pluck off all the florets which were in bloom, and then put the hard little head down inside their blouse. After an hour they looked at it again, and if the unexpanded florets had opened up and blossomed — they would be lucky in love! But what a ticklish business!

I am a hard and wiry tough little weed,
And grow in the grassland, where cows like to feed.
The cows dont like me, nor does the farmer,
Who tries to cut me, and finds that my armour,
Is just so tough that it blunts his shears,
And almost reduces the poor man to tears.
But I have my charms, and can soothe your sores,
So dont write me off as just one of those bores.

From the roadside by Novar, Evanton. August 1978

is for Lady's Mantle

Alchemilla filicaulis

This flower belongs to the Rosaceae family, (ROSE-A-SAY) and there is one cousin we all know very well the rose.

In days of old there were men who were called Alchemists, who studied medievat chemistry, and this was their favorite flower. They thought it was magical and held many secrets, and as you can see from its latin name, they called it after them- selves, adding "illa" as an endearment and meaning "The little Magical one".

Alchemists were always searching for the "Philosophers Stone" which they thought would turn baser metals into gold, for which man always sought. So they collected the pearly drops from the leaves of the Lady's Mantle, which they called "water from heaven" hoping this would hold the secret, but all in vain.

These pearly drops incidently are not all rain and dewdrops, as the plant exudes some moisture itself.

This herb was claimed by Venus, and was known as the friend of woman, and it was said by Culpepper, the herbalist, that ladies should drink distilled Lady's Mantle Water for twenty days to encourage conception. Infact all herbalists seemed keen on this flower, and Gerard says that the Alchemilla "keepeth down maidens paps and dugs, when they become too great and flaggie, it maketh them lesser and harder". So girls now you know!

Where woman toils and woman breathes,
I bring relief, through my dew drop leaves.
I'm the womans friend when she's in pain.
I even help, when her thoughts are vain,
And she wishes to reduce her paps,
In order to seduce the chaps.
The Alchemist also searched in vain
For the Philosopher's Stone with my drops of rain.
But for man himself I did withhold
The secret he wished in his search for gold.

Lady's Mantle   Alchemilla

Picked from the burnside infront of Old Allangrange House   July 80

M is for Marigold

Chrysanthemum segetum

This is the Corn Marigold, and it belongs to the COM-POS-IT-AE family, so it is the cousin of the daisy, we have already seen earlier in this book.   It grows in the corn fields, and the farmers consider it rather a weed, but its a very cheerful sight in the late summer. In the olden days before people had watches, they used to say you could tell the time by the Marigold which was said to keep its face to the sun as it goes round in the sky.   I picked this Marigold in September by the side of the road at Tore.

But here is something else which starts with the letter "M". Its a little Mouse.   Do you know what this little Mouse is called?" She is called Marion - I wonder why

My name is Marion, I'm a little mouse,
I live in the kitchen at Wayton House.
I am a gourmet for food,
And when in the mood,
Enjoy music, especially Wagner and Strauss.

Picked at Tore road junction September 78.

is for Nettle

Lanium purpureum

This nettle, the Red Deadnettle, belongs to the Labiatae (LAB-I-ATE-AY) family, which curiously does not include the Stinging Nettle, (Urtica dioica), which is the nettle we know best and about which I am mostly going to write.

The Stinging Nettle lives with man, with his rubbish and where ever he disturbs the ground. It clings to his dwellings long after man has gone and they are just ruins, which lead to the belief of the Highlanders that it grew from the bodies of dead men.

It has long been used as a fibre for weaving cloth, from the days of the early Egyptians until quite recently in Europe. Nettlecloth which was not coarse, but fine and strong, was woven much in Scotland and the poet Thomas Campbell (1777-1844) writes of sleeping in Nettle sheets.

Both the Red Deadnettle and Stinging Nettle make a very good vegetable rather like spinach, if the leaves are picked when they are young. Wear gloves when you pick the latter! I often fed your mother on this.

It was long a popular belief that nettle stings stimulated all organisms. Children were always told, when they were badly stung by nettles, how healthy they would always be, and how they would never have rheumatism.

The Roman Poet Petronius held that nettles increased virility and used to get someone to beat him with bunches of nettles below the navel. They even had a word for this "Nettle Beating" which was "Urtication" which was said to be good for ones general health.

It was also said that when the Romans first came to Britain, it was the only way they could keep themselves warm and stimulated.

When the Romans first left the Italian sun,
And embarked for Britain, their faces were glum,
As they'd heard of these Isles, and had also been told,
How damp it was, and how foggy and cold.
All this they found was horribly true,
They were permantly cold and permantly blue.
So to tingle their skins, they applied "Urtication"
To get themselves warm and achieve stimulation.

EC 80

Allangrange Kitchen Garden   March 80.

O is for Orchid

Dactylorhiza maculata.

The family is Orchidaceae, pronounced OR-KID-AY-SAY

The name orchid comes from the Greek word órkis, and orchid it gradually became, as it is easier to say.

The orchid has for a long time been connected with love and love potions, and it was said in mythology to be used by Satyrs, those wicked, lustful, shaggy divinities of the dark woods. They used to brew love potions from the root of the orchid until quite recently in Shetland and Ireland.

Another very different story about this. It is said that it was flowering at Gethsemane under the Cross, and that its leaves were spattered with the blood of Christ, and that it bears these spots to this day.

Our native Orchids are not like those splendid large exotic plants from the tropics, which you see in the most expensive shops in London. However we have a lot of small and very appealing little orchids. This one is the Moorland Spotted Orchid, and there is another one, very like this one, and quite common, called the Early Spotted Orchid. If you dig up the Early Spotted Orchid, you will find two tubers, which look like small bags, in which it stores its food. It was this curious root formation, which is the reason for all the many different names it was called locally, both curious and some a little rude perhaps! Here are some of them:-

Bloody mans Fingers, Candlesticks and Bones,
Granfer griggle Sticks, and Little Doggie Stones.
Long Purples, Bull Bags, Essex's Cuckoo Cocks,
Curly-Doddie, Kettle Cap and Stones of a Fox.
Aaron's Beard, Adders Tongue, quacking Ducks and Drake,
Ram's Horn Spotted Dog, and Flowers of a snake.
Cain and Abel, Giddy gander and Old Keet Legs,
Priest pintel, Puddock's spindles and Scotch Bull seggs.

Collected from up the back road July 1977

is for Poppy

Papaver rhoeas

The Poppy belongs to the Papaveraceae (PAPA-VER-A-SAY) family, and it is a cousin of the Fumitory, who we have already met, although this is strange as they look so very different.

Alas our lovely red Poppy has been driven from our cornfields by the weed killer.   In the old days it was a familiar sight in the corn, and if the cornfield was red with Poppies it was the sign of a good crop.   Infact the Roman Corn Goddess Ceres was always shown with a bunch of Corn and Poppies in her hand.

Our Poppy is harmless and contains no drugs like the Opium Poppy, however the seeds are used extensively in both European and Midde East cookery.

The Poppy likes to grow on disturbed ground which was why it sprung up after the plough and also why it appears on land that has been fought over.

As long ago as the 17th century fields of Poppies appeared at Neerwinden after the battle of that name between Luxembourg and William III on July 29th 1693.   Again as we all know they appeared in Flanders after the First World War, and which we remember by wearing Poppies on the 11th November each year.

The cornflower and I used to grow in the corn,
Along time ago, before you were born.
But that was before the day of the spray,
Which has virtually swept us both away.
But I still appear where'er blood is shed,
To remind the living of those who are dead.
So on November 11th, I still have my day,
So please buy a Poppy and for the dead pray
That never again may we pay such a price
And demand from so many that supreme sacrifice.

cked in front of Dillington Farm House June 1977.

Q is for Queen of the Meadows

Filipendula ulmaria

Queen of the Meadows, or to give it its other popular name Meadowsweet, belongs to the Rosaceae family (ROSA-SAY). and is a cousin of Lady's Mantle whom you have just met a few pages back.

It is tall and graceful and flowers from June to August all over the country in marshes, meadows, and damp places. It has lovely silver backed leaves and a beautiful head of creamy frothy little flowers, which could grace any garden with pride, and it verily is a Queen of the Meadows. The flowers have a very strong sweet smell which can be rather sickly when there are a lot of them together, the whole plant has a nice fresh smell however.

Because of its sweet smell and freshness, it was much used in the old days to strew on the floors. In these early days there was no such thing as carpets and rugs, and little sanitation, so they liked to cover the floors with rushes and sweet smelling herbs.

You will be surprized to learn that the name Meadowsweet, did not have anything to do with a meadow. Its old English name was Meadwort or Meadsweet as it was used for sweetening the mead, which was the popular alcoholic drink in those days which they all made.

It is also a useful medical herb which is good for all kidney troubles, rheumatism, and infectious diseases. For once the treatment prescribed is rather pleasant "Take a few handfuls of fresh cut flowers, and soak them in a litre of red wine for several hours, and drink a glass with each meal. **Why not?**

The English of old were a hard working breed,
And these hard working men would relax with their mead.
They got quite merry on this home made brew,
And life took on a much rosier hue.
By sweetening the mead to a state of perfection,
I helped them forget their state of dejection.

Collected from roadside on the way to Munlochy. August 1979.

is for Ragged Robin

Lychnis flos-cuculi

also for Red Campion

Silene dioca.

These two plants are cousins and both belong to the family Caryophyllaceae (CARY-O-FIL-A-SAY) and really they are very similar to look at. In fact if you took a pair of scissors and snipped all round the petals of the Red Campion, you would have a flower looking very like Ragged Robin.

These two plants have never been used for anything down the ages, like so many of our other wild flowers. They have no medical use, and they do not provide any food for us. However for all that, they are full of charm and give us a lovely show of colour in the Summer. The Red Campion, (which used to be called Champion in by gone days) can be seen in flower from May till November if the Autumn is mild. The Ragged Robin is more reluctant to flower, and only blossoms from May to June, when the Cuckoo is with us, which is why it was given the latin name of Lychnis flos-cuculi. The great difference between these two plants is where they grow. The Campion likes sunny banks and our hedgerows, where as the Ragged Robin likes the damp and Marsh lands.

It is meant to be very unlucky to pick either of these flowers, and it is said if you pick the Red Campion, you kill your father, but if you pick the White Campion, the mother dies. So pick neither please!! Heres an old tongue twister, slightly altered:-

Round and round the ragged rocks, the ragged Robin ran.
Say that many times, just as quickly as you can.
Why the Ragged Robin ran, and round those rocks did tear,
I dont know, and you dont know, and neither do we care.

Campion picked at Dillington 27ᵃ May 78

Ragged Robin picked Munlochy Bay 30ˣ June 80

EL . 78 . 80

is for Scabious

Knautia arvensis

This flower belongs to a family we have not met before called Dipsacaceae. (DIP-SA-KAE-SAE)
It is called after the Apothecaries Latin Scabiosa, which means a plant for scabs. Infact in the past it was simply known as the Scab Herb, as its juices were said to cure the scab the mange and the itch. How unattractive, and there seems to be no medical backing for this theory. How much nicer is its second common name - Gipsy Rose.
It is winter now as I write this, and ofcourse there are no Scabious in flower, which is sad, as I have just read in one of my reference books that this pale blue flower turns bright green at the touch of a lighted match. I cant wait to try
A local name for Scabious is Batchelors Buttons, and the girls would pick a few Scabious buttons and name each one after a boy friend, and then she chose her husband by the one which flowered best. It sounds as if he did'nt have much choice! Perhaps it happened in Leap year!

I make my appearance in early June,
At the time the cuckoo changes tune.
I like to be warm, and not to freeze,
And really prefer living south of the Tees.
In the olden days, which was very strange
They thought I cured both scab and mange.
I always disliked this claim to fame,
And whats more I dislike my horrid name.

The second flower shown opposite is Bindweed (Convolvulus arvensis.)

Both picked beside road between Taunton and Hatchbeauchamp
July 1979

EC

T is for Travellers Joy

Clematis vitalba

This plant belongs to the Ranunculaceae (RAN-UN-QU-LACE-AY) family and is a cousin of the Buttercup, who I am sure you know.

Gerard, the herbalist says "A plant decking and adorning waies and hedges where people travell and there upon I have named it Travellers Joie." And so it has been called ever since, but it has a second name, Old Man's Beard, which is descriptive of its seedhead in the Autumn.

I was known as Travellers Joy in those glorious days of old
As I rambled up and down the crooked English road.
I saw man go to work, and cheered him on his way,
I saw his tired return, and helped him end the day.
Alas those peaceful days are gone for me and also man.
Everyone's got to get there, as quickly as they can.
The ditch has gone, where hid the little simple sedges
They poison all the roadsides, and they clip and cut my hedges.
All I have to grow on now are barbed fences or the ground,
And there are hardly any corners left for man to roll around.
Where travellers loitered down my lane, after closing hours,
They motor past so fast today, they do not see my flowers.
Its hard to e'en imagine, those happy days of yore,
When you went to Plymouth Hove by way of Aviemore.

Picked in the old Front Drive, Dillington Park   July 1979

is for Umbelliferae

This page is different from the others, because I have said that "U" stands for Umbelliferae (UM-BELL-I-FUR-AY) which is not a flower, but is the name of a very large family of flowers. You may think this is a very long and difficult word but its quite easy if you think of an Umbrella, as the words are very alike. and the flower is just like a small umbrella. If you look at the picture above and opposite, you will see the flowers look very like an umbrella which has been turned inside out by the wind.

We grow many plants of this large family in our gardens, either as vegetables or herbs, such as carrots, parsley, parsnips, celery, angelica, dill, fennel, anice, chervil, caraway, and coriander. I show two here from the hedgerows, Cowparsley also known as Queen Anne's Lace and the Hogweed on the opposite page. There are two Hogweeds, this one and a giant one, which grows taller than your father. Beware of picking or cutting this giant though, as its juices can cause severe blisters.

A modern french author and healer says the leaves and crushed roots of the Hogweed, are very effective for curing boils, ulcers and insect bites. He also says it is one of the best aphrodisiacs, so perhaps that is why the pig farmers, who gave the plant its name used to feed it to their pigs. Lucky pigs!

I'm called the umbrella plant,
And have quite domestic habits.
There are simply hundreds of us.
As we multiply like rabbits!

Parsnips, parsley, celery and carrots
Will be the garden plants you know
Which if not devoured by maggots
Are not very hard to grow.

On the other side of the garden wall
I can be even more prolific.
Sweet Cicely, Hemlock, Queen Ann's Lace,
And that Hogweed so horrific.

This is to mention but only a few,
I could list my family for ever.
We never have minded where we grew
And can survive through any weather.

Collected in the lane leading to Hurst Farm, Hampshire. June 79.

V is for Vetch

Vicia cracca

This belongs to the leguminosae family (LEG-OOM-IN-O-SAY) This is a relation of the Clover, whom you are going to meet on the last page, and also of the garden Sweet pea, and the pea you eat.

There are quite a few vetches which grow in this country, but this one, the Tufted Vetch, I think is quite the most attractive, as it can have as many as over **30 lovely blue flowers in one cluster.** It likes to scramble and grow through hedges and bushes, and I encourage it to grow up my yew hedge in the garden - but not in my flower beds, its a weed there! When is a weed not a weed? When it grows where you want it.

Most authors seem to consider this flower as some what of a nonentity as it is of little use and has little history. The only Vetch, (or Tares, as they used to be called) they consider is of any use is the Common Vetch (Vicia sativa) which was introduced by the farmer for cattle fodder. However if the Tufted Vetch is unwise enough to grow up through the hedge into the field, the cows will soon have it.

I am one of those rather entangling weeds
Who makes good use of my neighbours I fear.
And I go through your garden, leaving my seeds
To make sure I come back the following year.

Alas in this world, I dont count for much
I've no cure for wounds, your fevers or itching.
I certainly havent the magical touch,
And gastronomically speaking I'm bad in the kitchen.

Picked in Allangrange Garden   August 1978.

W is for Wood Sorrel

Oxalis acetosella

This flower belongs to the Oxalidaceae family, and just has two cousins, both different sorrels. (OX-AL-I-DAY-SEE.)

This little flower which is common throughout the British Isles was often called the Alleluia Flower in the old days, as it comes out at Easter time and is a sign of delight and celebration. It is still known by this name in Italy and France. In this country in the early days it was commonly called "Sorrel de boys" as their pronunciation of the french "Sorrel de bois" was a little odd! However they eventually thought it would be much easer to call it by the English translation "Wood Sorrel."

This plant used to be cultivated to make sauce, and its leaves make a very good salad, the leaves taste much like the cultivated sorrel. Most children have bitten this flower and know the sharp pleasant taste. It was once considered a "must" for the Kitchen garden.

Some people think this plant is the original Shamrock leaf which was picked by St Patrick, while he was trying to explain to the people of Ireland the Holy Trinity and this little leaf divided in three was a visual explanation. Others say however it was not this flower but the clover. So who knows to whom the honour goes?

Where there are woods, I like to hide,
And make an appearance at Eastertide.
As they sing Alleluia on Easter Sunday,
I got that name, from all and sundry.
I'm still the "Alleluia Flower" in France,
Which does my little flower enhance.
But "Sorrel de bois" was my special name.
And in England "Sorrel de boys" it became.
Which makes me feel a bit of a freak
Oh why cant the "English learn to speak!

ed behind Redcastle April 1980.

EC. 80

is for eXTRA

Because I can't find a flower starting with "X" so I have chosen the periwinkle, the Latin name is Vinca minor and it belongs to the Apocynaceae family.

This is a flower which we readily accept in our gardens, it is a great ground cover plant, and I use it to cover the banks around my pond.

Curiously enough this flower shares its name with a sea snail, which we usually call a winkle for short. When I was a child at Dillington, we used to collect them off the rocks at Lyme Regis and bring them home, boil them, and with help of a pin to extract them, eat them for tea. But I am digressing, I should be writing about flowers not sea snails!

The periwinkle was brought to this country years ago as a medical herb. It was said to be especially good for piles, bleeding noses, and toothache, and herbalists still use it today. However its chief merit in the eyes of the ancients, was that it produced love between wife and husband. There is an old manuscript which says "Pervinca powdered with earth worms, induces love between husband and wife if they take it first with their food". What a threat!

In Italy, wreaths of periwinkles were hung around the necks of those due to be executed, perhaps as they are evergreens as a sign of immortality, but they became the 'Flower of death'. It is said that when Simon Fraser was executed in 1306, he wore a crown of periwinkles!

I have a little namesake, for whom please shed a tear,
He has a rather grand name, Littorina littorea.
But for me, he's just a winkle, you gather by the sea,
And take him home, and boil him and have him for your tea.
But I have nought to do with such funny little creatures,
Which ofcourse you see, when you gaze upon my features.
My flowers of violet blue and such glossy leaves of green,
Which cover, in the garden, those spots you don't want seen.
They brought me to this land for my medical connections,
I can even stop your toothache and cure a few infections.
So forget that Periwinkle, you have to boil and chew,
Of both the Periwinkles, I'm the better of the two.

Picked Allangrange Garden April 1979.

is for Yarrow

Achillea millefolium

    This flower belongs to the Compositae family (COM-POS-IT-AE) and has the daisy as one of its many cousins.

    It has long been used as a medical herb, which was especially renowned for healing wounds caused by iron and steel.   So in the old days when wars were fought with arrows and swords, it was much in use.

    At Troy that great warrior Achilles was shot in the heel by a poisoned arrow, which was the only place of his body where he could be wounded because he had been held by the heel and dipped in the River Styx as a baby by his mother, to protect him from all wounds.   He was told to dress his wound with Yarrow, by the Goddess Aphrodite, and he did, but the wound was mortal so he died, but gave his name to this flower, for its great healing powers.   We remember the brave Achilles by the vital tendon in our heel, which is so important to us and especially to athletes, and we call it our Achilles tendon.

The Gods gave Achilles their blessing at birth,
Forecasting a life of great merit and worth.
From his earliest youth in that Ancient Greece,
He learned that his life, would be no life of peace.
Whilst still a babe, and as yet in the manger,
Thetis, his mother, saw his life full of danger.
She took him up by the heel, inspite of his kicks
And completly immersed him in the great River Styx.
This made him immortal, where'er he might fight,
Except for the heel, Thetis lay hold of so tight.
In Achilles life, war played a great part,
It was his first love, his skill and his art.
He had loyalty, strength and never knew fear,
And by all who fought with, he was held very dear.
He fought to his death, ever brave ever bold,
But was shot in the heel, as had been foretold.

Collected up the back road   October 1977

is for Zig zag Clover.

Trifolium medium

The Clover belongs to the Leguminosae (LEG-OOM-IN-O-SAY) family, so is a cousin of the Vetch

This is one of the most valuable feeding crops for cattle and the farmers grow it for this purpose.   In the old days it was not called Clover but Claver, which is why we have so many villages and places called "Claver" such as Claverdon, Claverton and Clavering.

Clovers have always been lucky, but a four leafed clover was known to be especially lucky, as it was a symbol of the Holy Cross. To have and to hold a four leafed clover was said to bring you luck and to protect you from danger and to have miraculous powers.

Here is a story about a clover, which I hope you enjoy, its not "quite" a fairy story:-

Once upon a time there was a little clover who lived on the Black Isle in Ross-shire.   She was a Zigzag Clover and rather special, as there are not very many "Zigzags" who grow about there.

She grew at the edge of a field, just outside the field fence, and had a lovely view of Munlochy Bay one way, and on the other side, there was a small back road, where she could watch the occasional person walk, perhaps with a dog or gun, sometimes both,   also cars and cows occasionally passed that way, when they were changing fields.

But ofcourse what went on in "her" field as she called it, was what mattered most to her,   Some years they grew barley in it, and she would watch it be sown, and then come up, and have to watch those naughty rabbits eat it when it was young.
However a lot survived, and it would grow tall, and change its

Collected off the wall by roadside near Allanglach June 1980

colour, and then combines would move in and harvest it.

However she liked it best field was in grass, and the cows grazed there. She got to know them all so well, and saw all their calves arrive, and grow up and frisk around and she loved them all.

She realized also how very lucky she was to live just the other side of the fence, as she could see all that was going on, yet was not ploughed up each year that they planted the barley, and also, though the odd cow could reach her through the fence, she was not eaten by all the cows all the time.

However Clover knew that being eaten by cows was part of a clovers job in life, as it provided them with the nourishment they needed to produce their milk. So that is why, every year, clovers part with their flowers and leaves, and let the cows eat them, and then grow more leaves and flowers.

Though Clover did not mind the cows eating her leaves, she did object to the rabbits when they ate them, as they were rather cheeky, and did not provide anything for anybody, and she did not think it was part of her job to nourish them. Anyway they ate more young grass and young barley than they should.

Of all her cows, as she called them, there was a special one, who was called Clara, with whom she was specially friendly. Clara was rather shy and spent a lot of time by herself and talked to Clover a lot, as she had no calf and so had lots of time. But she told Clover how she was very sad she had no calf, and how she longed to have one.

Spring went however, and Summer came and still Clara had no calf, and she came to Clover one day in great distress, and said she was very unhappy because she had no calf, and felt she was under a cloud, and she thought something terrible would happen to her if she remained barren and did'nt have one. She had heard from the other cows, that Bobbie, who looked after them all, did'nt like barren cows and sent them to be sold in the market, and she did'nt want to go away and be sold in the market. So Clover tried to cheer her up and comfort her, and told her to come back in a weeks time, and meanwhile she would see if she could have a bright idea. Now four leaf clovers, are as you know very lucky, and Clover thought she would try and grow one for Clara. She did, and when Clara came back, she told her to put her head through the fence and to eat the four leafed clover she had grown for her and to make a wish. Well Clara did exactly as she was told, and I think

we can guess what she wished, but ofcourse she didn't tell anybody.

Soon after this the winter came and the cold weather and the snow, and Bobbie took all the cows out of the field and put them in a nice warm yard for the winter. Clover's leaves and flowers died back and she went to sleep for the winter.

When Clover woke up it was spring, and to her great joy the cows were already back in the field, and there waiting for her by the fence was a very happy Clara. "Oh" said Clara "I thought you were never going to wake up, and I have been longing to tell you my great news, I am going to have a calf is'nt that wonderful."

Clover agreed with her, and was very delighted to hear the good news and to know that her little bit of magic had worked. She was even more thrilled when a little later on, Clara came over to the corner of the field where she lived, and gave birth to a lovely little white calf.

Oh Clara was so thrilled and so proud of her white calf, who she thought was the most beautiful calf she had ever seen. She should not have been so surprized at having such a beautiful white calf, as though she herself was a pale dun colour, perhaps not all that handsome, if truth were told, the father of the calf was a handsome Charolais bull by the name of "Goldie's Magician". So with a Magician for a father, and helped by Clover's magic, the calf was just total magic, anyway in Clara's eyes.

Clara was so grateful to Clover for the help she had given her, and thanked her over and over again, and asked her if she could call her calf "Clover" after her. Clover said "Well I think there are rather a lot of 'Clovers' and as I am a Zigzag Clover, and my magic helped her, why not call her Magical Zigzag Clover?" Well this ofcourse was far too long a name for a small calf, so everyone just called her "Zaggie".

So Zaggie soon began to grow and became big and strong, and she had a lovely spring, and she used to love running races and playing with all the other calves in the field. After her games and when her legs were tired, she liked to go and lie near Clover and listen to the lovely stories she told.

Then quite suddenly Zaggie did not want to play or listen to stories, she was not happy and she did not know why. She did not want to eat or drink her mother's milk, and she grew thinner and thinner. Clara got so worried, but however hard she tried, she could not persuade Zaggie to eat or drink.

Bobbie got very worried too, as no one could think what was wrong

with Zaggie.   So Bobbie sent for Hamish the vet, who came and gave
poor Zaggie an injection, which she didn't like a bit, and alas it did not seem
to cure her and she just got thinner than ever.
    Ofcourse Clara told Clover all about her worries every day, and eventually
she began to despair and thought poor Zaggie would die.   Then Clover had
a bright idea, and she wondered if she could grow another four leafed clover
and if they could persuade Zaggie to eat it she might be cured.
    So she not say anything to Clara until she had grown the leaf, and
then she told her.   Clara was delighted and went to fetch Zaggie,
who was lying in another part of the field.   She persuaded her to
get up, and with great difficulty she managed to get her to cross the field
to Clovers corner.   Then aftershe had had a rest, they tried to
make her put her head through the fence and eat the four leafed clover.
    Then the problems began, because poor little Zaggie's neck, was not
long enough to reach the clover.   "Oh dear" said Clover, "Oh dear" said
Clara, "what ever shall we do now".   "Well I cant move" said Clover,
"but where there is a will there is a way, so Clara you must just push Zaggie
through the fence".
    So Clara pushed and shoved with all her might, and eventually she
loosened a post and managed to push a reluctant Zaggie through.
Once she was through, Zaggie just wanted to sleep, but Clover made her take
a nibble at the leaf, and then another, until it was all gone.   Then she
just lay where she was beside Clover and went to sleep.
    And that is where Bobbie found her the next morning, and he could not
understand why she was there, or how a small sick calf could do so
much damage to the fence.!   He lifted her gently back into the field
beside Clara, and Zaggie was glad, and before going to sleep again, she took
a little drink of warm milk and felt a little better.
    After a week she felt much better and she began to eat and drink again,
and she started to grow again also.   Clara made her go and say thank you
to Clover through the fence.   She couldnt get through as it had been mended.
    When winter came again and it was time for all the cows to leave the field,
Zaggie had quite recovered, and after that, she never looked back.
    Clover saw them quite often, over the next few years, Clara had
another calf, this time without the help of Clover and she was very
pleased.   Then one day, Zaggie who was quite grown up now and
a very beautiful cow, came and whispered to Clover that she was going to
have a calf.   "Well well" said Clover and so the world goes on.

Zaggie grown up.

A *Webb&Bower* BOOK
Edited, designed and produced by
Webb & Bower (Publishers) Limited, Exeter, England

Jacket design by Peter Wrigley

Canadian Cataloguing in Publication Data
Cameron, Elizabeth.
A floral ABC

ISBN 0–471–79830–4
1. Wild flowers.   2. Plant lore.   I. Title.

QK85.5.C35   582.13   C82–094584–6

Printed and bound in Hong Kong by Mandarin Offset International Limited